Old MacDonald

SO-AWZ-123

Cover illustration by JON GOODELL

Illustrations by
KRISTA BRAUCKMANN-TOWNS
JANE CHAMBLESS WRIGHT
DREW-BROOK-CORMACK ASSOCIATES
KATE STURMAN GORMAN
JUDITH DUFOUR LOVE
BEN MAHAN
ANASTASIA MITCHELL
ANITA NELSON
ROSARIO VALDERRAMA

Louis Weber, C.E.O.
Publications International, Ltd.
7373 North Cicero Avenue
Lincolnwood, Illinois 60646

Manufactured in U.S.A.

8 7 6 5 4 3 2 1

ISBN: 0-7853-1651-5

PUBLICATIONS INTERNATIONAL, LTD.

The Hobbyhorse

I had a little hobbyhorse,
  And it was dapple gray;
Its head was made of pea-straw,
  Its tail was made of hay.

I sold it to an old woman
  For a copper penny;
And I'll gladly sing my song again
  If your horse should whinny!

The Piper and His Cow

There was a piper had a cow,
    And he had nothing to give her;
He pulled out his pipes and played her a tune,
    And asked the cow to consider.

The cow considered very well,
    And gave the piper some money,
And asked him to play another tune,
    That she would find quite funny.

Old MacDonald

Old MacDonald had a farm, E-I-E-I-O.
  And on this farm he had some cows, E-I-E-I-O.

With a moo-moo here and a moo-moo there,
  Here a moo, there a moo, everywhere a moo-moo.

Old MacDonald had a farm, E-I-E-I-O.
  And on this farm he had some donkeys, E-I-E-I-O.

With a hee-haw here and a hee-haw there,
  Here a hee, there a haw, everywhere a hee-haw.

Old MacDonald had a farm, E-I-E-I-O.
  And on this farm he had some pigs, E-I-E-I-O.

With an oink-oink here and an oink-oink there,
  Here an oink, there an oink, everywhere an oink-oink.

Old MacDonald had a farm, E-I-E-I-O.

There Was a Little Pig

There was a little pig,
  Who wasn't very big,
So they put him in a great big show.
  While playing in the band,
He broke his little hand,
  And now he can't play his old banjo.

The Donkey

Donkey, donkey, old and gray,
  Open your mouth and gently bray;
Lift your ears and blow your horn,
  To wake the world this sleepy morn.

Bell Horses

Bell horses, bell horses,
   What time of day?
One o'clock, two o'clock,
   Three and away.

Robert Barnes

Robert Barnes, fellow fine,
　　Can you shoe this horse of mine?
Yes, good sir, that I can,
　　As well as any other man.
There's a nail, and there's a prod,
　　And now, good sir, your horse is shod.

A Horse and a Flea

A horse and a flea and three blind mice
    Met each other while skating on ice.
The horse he slipped and fell on the flea.
    The flea said, "Oops, there's a horse on me!"

Charlie Warlie

Charlie Warlie had a cow,
　　Black and white around the brow;
Open the gate and let her in,
　　Charlie's cow is home again.

Dickery, Dickery, Dare

Dickery, dickery, dare,
    The pig flew up in the air;
The man in brown soon brought him down,
    Dickery, dickery, dare.

Upon My Word

Upon my word and honor
    As I went to Bonner,
I met a pig
    Without a wig,
Upon my word and honor.

The Purple Cow

I never saw a purple cow,
   I hope I never see one;
But I can tell you, anyhow,
   I'd rather see than be one.